The sun was shining.
Ramu and Sita went out.
They went into the town.

1

Ramu and Sita met
an old man.
The old man had a donkey.

Ramu and Sita saw a big red bus.
The donkey saw the bus.

3

The donkey ran away.
The old man ran after
the donkey.

The donkey ran up the hill.
The old man ran up the hill.
He ran after the donkey.

The donkey ran down the hill.
The old man ran down the hill.
He ran after the donkey.

The donkey saw Ramu and Sita.

The old man went home
with the donkey.